Buc
ind

VWW

I HERO

Death or Glory!

Steve Barlow and Steve Skidmore

Illustrated by Sonia Leong

W

FRANKLIN WATTS

LONDON•SYDNEY

First published in 2007
by Franklin Watts

Franklin Watts
338 Euston Road
London NW1 3BH

Franklin Watts Australia
Level 17/207 Kent Street
Sydney, NSW 2000

A CIP catalogue record for this book
is available from the British Library.

ISBN: 978 0 7496 7664 3

1 3 5 7 9 10 8 6 4 2

Printed in Great Britain

Franklin Watts is a division of Hachette Children's Books,
an Hachette Livre UK company.

Decide your own destiny...

This book is not like others you may have read. *You* are the hero of this adventure. It is up to you to make decisions that will affect how the adventure unfolds.

Each section of this book is numbered. At the end of most sections, you will have to make a choice. The choice you make will take you to a different section of the book.

Some of your choices will help you to complete the adventure successfully. But choose carefully, some of your decisions could be fatal!

If you fail, then start the adventure again and learn from your mistake.

If you choose correctly you will succeed in your adventure.

Don't be a zero, be a hero!

You are a warrior living on the island of Britannia – today called Great Britain.

It is almost 37 years since the Romans invaded Britannia. Their forces have conquered most of the country.

You are part of a tribe locked in a bitter struggle with the Romans. You have already proved your bravery by leading many daring raids against the armies of Rome, burning their camps and driving them back from your lands.

But now, a powerful Roman army has arrived and it is about to attack your stronghold. If they win, Britain will become a Roman province. Any Britons who survive the battle will be captured and sold as slaves.

You are sharpening your sword in readiness for the battle when you are called to a meeting with the chief of your tribe.

Now turn to section 1.

1

The chief is waiting for you in the great hall.

"The Roman army is nearby," he says, "but we don't know where. The scouts I sent out to spy on the enemy have not returned. If I cannot find the Roman army, I cannot prepare my defences.

"You have proved your bravery many times. I need you to go and find the Romans. I want you to bring me news of where they are, and the size of their army."

If you agree to spy on the Romans, turn to 13. If you don't wish to, turn to 35.

2

You shake hands. Lupus smiles and walks away.

Verus comes over to talk to you. "Be careful," he tells you. "I don't trust Lupus."

"Why not?" you ask.

"Festus pays him to keep an eye on everything that happens here. And he's friendly with Crixus. I'm giving you this advice as a friend. Stay clear of him."

As you leave the training ground, Lupus offers you a drink.

If you accept the drink, go to 9.
If you refuse the drink, go to 49.

3

You know that if you are bought by a gladiator trainer, you will find it very difficult to escape. "Oh, no, master," you say in a trembling voice, "I'm no warrior. I'm very weak."

"I thought so. He's no use to me," Festus tells the slave-trader. "Send him to the lead mines."

Your heart sinks. The other slaves have told you all about the mines. No one leaves there alive.

The slave-trader takes off your chains.

If you decide to attack him, go to 48.
If you decide not to resist, go to 10.

4

"Don't tell me what to do," you say.

Verus gives you a hard look. Without warning, he knocks you to the ground. As you roll in the sand, Verus put his foot on your chest and holds his wooden sword to your throat. "Only a fool ignores good advice," he says. Then he throws the sword down and walks off.

Go to 10.

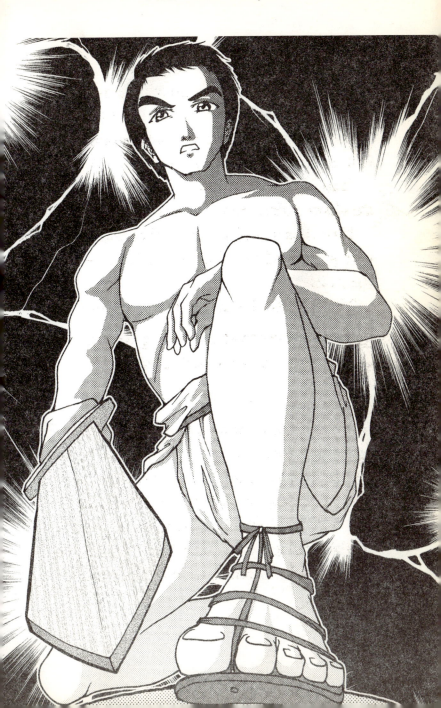

5

The guards take you and Verus to Festus.

"You have cost me two gladiators," he snarls. "I shall send you both to the amphitheatre – to fight to the death before the Emperor!"

"Verus is my friend," you tell Festus. "I don't want to fight him."

"Gladiators do not choose who they fight!" says Festus. He signals to the guards. "Take them away!"

If you accept your punishment, go to 12.
If you want to beg for mercy, go to 45.

6

As the guards lead you through the crowded streets, a chariot appears. It is going fast. You and the guards jump out of the way to avoid being run down and in the confusion, you escape.

You cut through alleyways, but the guards are soon on your trail. You can hear their shouts and pounding feet behind you.

You sprint out of an alleyway and find yourself in the Forum, the great marketplace of Rome. Before you can lose yourself in the crowds, you trip over and crash into a vegetable stall. The angry guards recapture you and haul you away.

Go to 14.

7

You give Crixus a hard look. You want to pay him back for his insults. "I'll fight Crixus."

Crixus grins. "Suits me, slave. Prepare to die!"

The fight begins. Crixus is strong and fast. Several times, the point of his sword cuts you. Soon you are bleeding heavily. You realise that Crixus is toying with you. He could finish you off at any time.

In desperation, you fling the net. It is a lucky throw and brings Crixus down. You hold your trident to his throat.

If you decide to tell Crixus to surrender, go to 24.

If you decide to step back and allow him to get up, turn to 27.

8

You and Bran travel through the night. Just before dawn, you both climb a hill. On the other side you see the Roman camp. As the sun rises, you can see the strength of the Roman force. "At least six hundred tents," you tell Bran, "with eight men in each. There must be a full legion down there, nearly 5,000 men. Far too many for us to fight. We have to get back and warn the chief."

But at that moment you hear shouts. A Roman patrol has found you.

If you decide to try to escape, go to 21.
If you decide to surrender, go to 40.

9

"Thanks," you say, taking the drink.

Lupus turns out to be very friendly and helpful. Later, he helps you mend your net. He brings you food from the kitchen, too.

One day, when you are sitting in the communal toilet, he comes up to you. "Listen," he whispers, "there's going to be a revolt. We gladiators are going to escape. There's a meeting tonight in the Forum. Will you come?"

If you say yes, go to 17.

If you say no, go to 49.

10

Festus looks at you with scorn. "A fool and a weakling," he scoffs. He calls his guards. "Take him to the mines!"

You end up in a chain gang, digging poisonous lead ore. The work is back-breaking. You are beaten and starved. There is no escape, and you know you will not last long.

You are not the hero you thought you were. If you wish to begin again, turn to 1.

11

"What's going on here?" demands Festus.

"I was just teaching this dog some manners," snarls Crixus.

The gladiator who broke up the fight shakes his head. "This man has only just arrived. I'm sure he meant no harm."

"You are too ready to fight for no reason, Crixus," says Festus. "Get on with your training." Crixus scowls at you before he storms away.

The gladiator holds out his hand. "My name is Verus."

Go to 20.

12

You are waiting with Verus to go into the huge amphitheatre.

Two gladiators are already fighting. As you watch, one falls.

Verus points up to a man watching the fight. He is dressed in a fine, purple toga. "That's the Emperor. If he turns his thumb up, the beaten man will live. If he turns it down, he will die."

The Emperor raises his hand, and turns his thumb down. The winner thrusts with his sword. The crowd cheers.

Then it is your turn. You and Verus march out onto the sand of the amphitheatre. You halt before the Emperor. "Hail, Caesar!" you shout together. "We who are about to die salute you!"

The Emperor signals for the fight to begin.

If you decide to attack Verus at once, go to 25.

If you decide to dodge and wear him down, go to 39.

13

"I knew I could count on you," says the chief. "But you will need help. I have already spoken to your friend Bran. He says he will go with you. If you think you need more men, you can take my bodyguards. That will give you 20 good men, armed and ready to fight. Well, then? My bodyguards or Bran. Which shall it be?"

If you choose the bodyguards, go to 47.
If you choose Bran, go to 8.

14

You arrive at Festus's training school. The guards take you to a courtyard. Several gladiators are fighting each other with wooden swords.

The guards shove you forward and you lose your balance. You bump into one of the gladiators, who turns on you in fury.

"Blockhead!" he roars. "Clumsy fool! How dare you lay hands on the great Crixus."

If you decide to apologise, go to 23.

If you decide to stand up to Crixus, go to 43.

15

You get into the routine of training. Soon, you are winning practice fights against the other gladiators. But Crixus refuses to fight you, and you haven't yet beaten Verus.

After a practice session, a gladiator called Lupus offers you his hand.

"You're much too good for me," he says. "I'd much rather have you as a friend than an enemy. Shake on it?"

If you shake hands, go to 2.

If you do not want to shake hands, go to 49.

16

You point to the helmet. "I'll be a secutor."

But when you put the helmet on you can't see properly through the visor. The shield is heavy and it slows you down.

Verus shakes his head. "You're fast on your feet, and this gear is too heavy for you. I think you should be a retiarius."

If you decide to follow Verus's advice, turn to 37.

If you decide to continue as a secutor, turn to 4.

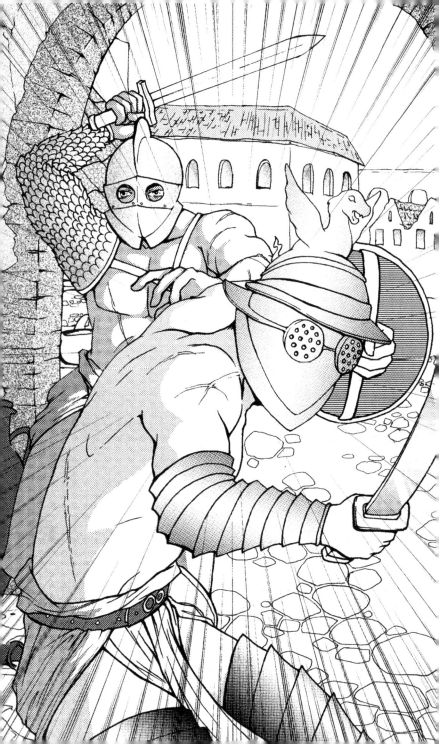

17

You make your way to the Forum. All the market traders have packed up their wares and it is deserted. Lupus is already there. "Where are the others?" you ask him.

He grins. "Here they are!" He whistles, and Crixus and some guards appear. "There's the traitor," cries Lupus, "arrest him!"

It's a trap!

Suddenly you hear a friendly voice. "Briton!" Verus has followed you. He thrusts a sword into your hand, and turns to face Crixus.

The fight is short and brutal, and the guards watch from a distance. Moments later, Lupus and Crixus lie dead on the stone pavement.

Go to 5.

18

You throw the net. It tangles around Verus's sword arm and helmet. You pull at the net with all your might, tearing Verus's sword from his hand and his helmet from his head. Verus is helpless and at your mercy.

If you decide to attack Verus, go to 22.
If you decide not to attack, go to 30.

19

"All right," Bran says. "Then I'll leave with you."

You have not gone far when you meet a crowd of villagers hurrying down the hill.

"Why are you running?" you ask.

An old man grabs your arm. "The Romans are coming. They have torched our village. If they catch us, they will kill us! If you have any sense, you'll come with us."

But it is too late. You look up and see Roman soldiers marching towards you.

If you decide to try to escape, go to 21.
If you decide to surrender, go to 40.

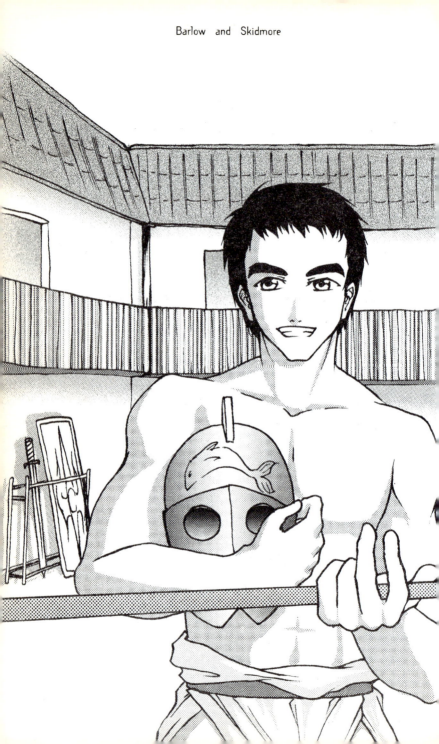

20

Festus gives you a sour look. "It seems you can't wait to start your training, Briton. We'd better find a fighting style for you."

Verus shows you a helmet with a picture of a fish on it. "You could be a secutor. You wear this helmet and carry a large sword and a tall shield – but be careful, the shield is heavy."

Then he picks up a three-pronged spear. "Or you could be a retiarius. You have armour on your left arm and shoulder, and you carry this trident and a net. Now choose."

If you want to be a secutor, turn to 16.
If you want to be a retiarius, turn to 37.

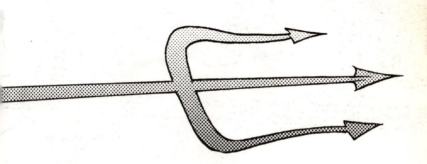

21

You and Bran run away, towards a forest where you will be able to hide. Roman soldiers chase you.

As you reach the bottom of the small hill, you find another Roman patrol waiting for you. You try to fight your way through them, but Bran gives a terrible cry as a Roman soldier cuts him down. You turn to help him, and feel a spear-tip at your throat. You have been captured.

Go to 33.

22

Your trident breaks on Verus's shield.

Verus rolls and picks up his sword. The tables are turned. You have no weapons.

You surrender to Verus and appeal to the Emperor.

The crowd boos. They think you have given in too easily. The Emperor agrees. He raises his hand and turns his thumb down, ordering Verus to kill you.

Verus hesitates. But the Emperor has decided. There is nothing he can do. He steps forward and swings his sword.

Your adventure has ended. If you wish to begin again, turn back to 1.

23

"I'm sorry," you say, "the guards pushed me and…"

You get no further. Crixus punches you hard in the stomach. You double over in pain. The other gladiators laugh.

If you decide to attack Crixus, go to 43.

If you want to crawl away, go to 10.

24

Festus laughs. "Well done. Not bad for a beginner. We'll make a gladiator of you yet."

Grinning, Verus offers you his hand in friendship. You take it.

Crixus gives you a look of pure hatred. Without meaning to, you have made a dangerous enemy.

Go to 15.

25

Your attack fails. Your trident just bounces off Verus's shield. Now you are too close to use your net.

Verus attacks, and beats you back. He is still faster and stronger than you.

You try to dodge, but you are too slow. Verus's sword slips through a gap in your defence. You feel a terrible pain in your side. The sounds of the arena fade, and the world goes dark.

Your adventure has ended. If you wish to begin again, turn back to 1.

26

You are furious. "This is my fight!" you cry. "Stay out of it!"

You take a wild swing at the gladiator, but he is too fast for you. He dodges backwards. You overbalance and fall to the ground.

The gladiator laughs. "Learn to fight like a gladiator before you tangle with one."

You realise that your temper has made you look foolish. "You're right," you say. "I'm sorry."

The gladiator helps you to your feet. "My name is Verus."

Go to 20.

27

Crixus fights clear of the net. A blow from his sword smashes your trident.

"Farewell, Briton!" yells Crixus. "Carry my greetings to Hades!"

His sword flashes once again. You feel a moment's terrible pain, and then darkness takes you.

Your first fight as a gladiator has also been your last. If you wish to begin again, turn back to 1.

28

You make it back safely to the stronghold. You report to the chief.

He shakes his head. "It was a mistake to take so many men," he says. "You'll never creep up on the Romans with a large force. But one or two brave men might get through. I want you and Bran to go and spy on the Romans."

You agree to go with Bran.

Turn to 8.

29

Verus attacks you. You dodge him easily and throw the net. Verus is caught.

As the other gladiators free Verus from the net, Festus nods with approval. "Good. You've chosen a style that suits you. But that was just a practice. Now, let's see what you're made of in a proper contest with real weapons. Who do you want to fight? Verus again, or Crixus?"

If you want to fight Crixus, turn to 7.
If you want to fight Verus, turn to 41.

30

You throw aside your trident.

Verus looks startled. Then he nods, and throws down his shield. The crowd applauds wildly. Now you are both even again.

You wrestle. Verus is stronger than you, but you are younger. You turn his attack into a throw, and Verus lies sprawled on the sand of the amphitheatre.

As you step forward, you stand on something hard. You look down, to see Verus's sword at your feet. You pick it up.

If you want to allow Verus to appeal to the Emperor, go to 50.

If you decide to finish Verus off, go to 34.

31

Festus isn't pleased when you take him to your room to show him the dead dog, and find it gone.

"I don't believe there ever was a dead dog," he says angrily. "Even if there was, I don't believe Lupus had anything to do with it."

He waves a finger at you. "I think you're a troublemaker. You'd better watch your step."

You are angry. You decide to go and see Lupus, and accuse him to his face.

Go to 36.

32

You lunge at Verus with your trident. He sweeps it aside with his shield, and jabs you in the shoulder. His wooden practice sword is too blunt to draw blood, but it still hurts.

Verus shakes his head. "Use your trident to keep my sword away, but your main weapon is the net. If you can get your opponent tangled up in that, he's helpless."

If you decide to ignore Verus's advice, go to 4.

If you decide to take Verus's advice, go to 29.

33

It is many weeks since you were captured. After a long journey crammed into a sailing ship and tied to a horse and cart, you have arrived in the great city of Rome – the centre of the Roman empire. You have never seen such a place, with its tall buildings and temples.

You are taken to the slave market. Here you stand with other captives from many lands. Wealthy Romans wander round deciding which slaves to buy.

The slave-trader points you out to one of his customers. "Look, Festus. A British slave, just arrived. He's the sort of fighting man to make a good gladiator."

The man called Festus examines you. "You look like a weakling to me, Briton. Do you think you're tough enough to be a gladiator?"

If you say yes, go to 38.
If you say no, go to 3.

34

You lunge with the sword. Verus lies dead on the sand. You have won.

But the crowd boo. The Emperor looks angry and turns his back on you. By killing Verus when he was helpless, you have shown that you have no honour.

When you leave the amphitheatre, Festus has you put in chains. "You will be back in the arena soon," he tells you, "when I have you thrown to the lions!"

There is no escape for you. You can start the adventure again by going back to 1.

35

"What chance have I got?" you ask the chief. "The Romans will know we're coming. I'm ready to die in battle, but what you're asking me to do is suicide!"

The chief is angry. "There is no place in my tribe for cowardly warriors!" he cries. "Get out of my sight!"

You pack your belongings and leave the stronghold. But as you reach the gates, your friend Bran calls you back. He has talked the chief into giving you one last chance.

If you want to change your mind and accept the mission, go to 13.

If you still want to refuse the chief's offer, go to 19.

36

You find Lupus on the training ground and accuse him.

"I don't know anything about a dead dog," says Lupus.

Crixus gives you a nasty grin. "He was with me all evening."

"You're both liars," you tell them.

"No man calls me a liar!" cries Lupus. He and Crixus both reach for their swords.

"Briton! Here!" Verus throws you a sword and turns to fight Crixus.

Moments later, Lupus and Crixus lie dead in the sand.

Go to 5.

37

You pull on the armoured sleeve and pick up the trident and the net. You have little to protect you, but you can move about quickly.

"Good," says Verus, "let's try a practice fight."

Verus puts on the secutor's helmet and picks up the practice sword and shield. You walk with him to the centre of the hot courtyard. You turn to face each other.

Do you try to jab Verus with your practice trident, or entangle him in your net?

If you decide to use the trident, turn to 32.
If you decide to use the net, turn to 29.

38

You glare at Festus. "No man calls me a weakling. Take off my chains, and you'll soon see how weak I am!"

Festus laughs. "This one has spirit! He'll do well in the arena. If he fights well he may even win his freedom." He takes out his purse and pays the slave-trader several gold coins.

The slave-trader calls out to his guards. "Remove this man's chains and take him to the gladiator school of Festus."

If you decide to go willingly with the guards, turn to 14.

If you decide to take this chance to escape, turn to 6.

39

You dodge, staying out of Verus's reach. You know you must keep moving to tire your opponent. Sometimes you dart in and jab with your trident. Sometimes you are too slow to escape Verus's sword.

You are both hurt. But the fight goes on. The crowd cheers. They have never seen such a contest.

Then Verus slips on a patch of fresh blood and falls to his knees.

If you decide to throw your net, go to 18.

If you decide to attack him with your trident, go to 42.

40

The Romans take you prisoner.

"British scum!" sneers a Roman officer. "I knew you would rather give in than fight."

Bran lifts his head proudly. "If you want a fair fight, Roman, call your men off and face me in single combat. Or are you a coward?"

The officer snarls and stabs Bran with his sword. You cry out as your friend drops down dead. A sword pommel smashes into the back of your head, and you fall to the ground, stunned.

Go to 33.

41

The fight begins.

Verus is a fast and clever fighter. You realise that he wasn't really trying in the practice bout. If he wanted to, Verus could win the fight at any time.

But as he moves in to attack, the strap on his sandal breaks and he stumbles. You throw the net and bring him down.

Do you attack Verus while he is helpless, or laugh and help him up?

If you decide to attack Verus, go to 46.
If you decide to help him up, go to 24.

42

You thrust at Verus with your trident. Verus manages to raise his shield in time and your trident glances off it. Your attack has failed.

But you realise that in beating off your attack, Verus has left his body unprotected.

Go to 18.

43

You throw yourself at Crixus and wrestle him to the ground. The other gladiators form a circle around you and cheer.

Festus appears. He looks angry. One of the gladiators spots him and hauls you off Crixus. "That's enough," the gladiator says. "Save your fighting for the arena."

If you want to fight the gladiator who stopped you attacking Crixus, go to 26.

If you don't want to, go to 11.

44

You and the chief's bodyguards fight bravely, but you are outnumbered. Your men are falling all around you. Soon, you are the last man standing and the Romans are closing in.

You see a standard-bearer carrying the banner of the Roman legion. You try to cut him down. But a heavy blow to the back of your head knocks you out and you fall to the ground.

Go to 33.

45

"Festus," you cry, "Verus will kill me. Have mercy!"

Verus gives you a disgusted look. Festus stares at you with scorn. "Worm!" he says. "You're not fit for the amphitheatre." He points to one of his guards. "Kill him!"

The guard draws his sword. The last thing you see is the light glinting on the blade as he swings it at your neck.

Your adventure has ended. If you wish to begin again, turn back to 1.

46

Verus rolls away and throws off the net. He parries your trident and holds his sword-point to your throat. "Is this how you repay my help?" he cries. "You deserve to die!"

But Festus shakes his head. "He is not worthy of your sword, Verus. He has no honour. He is no gladiator. I'll not waste my time training the likes of him."

Go to 10.

47

You set off with the chief's bodyguards. You have not gone far when you see a column of Roman soldiers coming over a hill.

There are too many of them to sneak past.

"We have two choices," you say to the bodyguards. "Fight the Romans, or abandon our mission and head back to the stronghold before they spot us."

If you decide to fight the Romans, go to 44.

If you decide to abandon your mission, go to 28.

47

48

The moment your hands are free, you hurl yourself at the slave-trader and rain blows on him. He cries for help. The guards come running and drag you off him.

Festus turns back with a grin, "So, Briton, you do have a spark of courage after all." He clicks his fingers at the guards. "Take him to my training school."

If you decide to go quietly, go to 14.
If you decide to try to escape, go to 6.

49

You shake your head. "I don't trust you, Lupus."

Lupus gives you a very unfriendly look. "You'll be sorry. If you're not my friend, you're my enemy." He strides away. A few minutes later, you see him talking to Crixus.

That night in the sleeping quarters, after a hard day's training, you spot a lump in your bed roll. Carefully, you pull back the blanket. You gasp at the stench.

Somebody has put a dead dog in your bed.

If you decide to report this to Festus, go to 31.

If you decide to accuse Lupus of putting the dog there, go to 36.

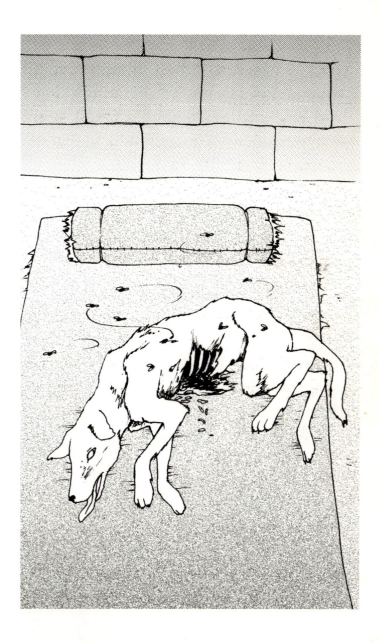

50

Verus bows his head to you. "I surrender." He appeals to the Emperor.

The Emperor raises both his hands. As you watch in amazement, he turns both his thumbs up. The crowd roars its approval.

The Emperor speaks, "You are both brave men and skilful gladiators. You have fought well. As a reward for your courage, I grant you both your freedom."

The crowd cheers as you shake hands with Verus. Together, you have cheated death. You are a hero!

If you enjoyed reading

Death or Glory!

there are more titles in the
I Hero series:

Viking Blood

978 0 7496 7665 0

Gorgon's Cave

978 0 7496 7666 7

Code Mission

978 0 7496 7667 4

Viking Blood

Steve Barlow and Steve Skidmore

Illustrated by Sonia Leong

It is the age of the Vikings. You are the captain of the trading ship, *Vidar*. You are sailing home to your village after a long voyage. It has been a good one. You have sold your cargo of hides and grain, and are bringing home weapons and pots that will make you a lot of money.

As your ship rounds a headland, one of your crew shouts out, "Captain, come quickly!"

You make your way to the front of your longship and stare towards land. You gasp in horror – all you can see is burnt timber and wrecked houses. Your village has been destroyed!

I HERO

DECIDE YOUR
OWN DESTINY

Viking
Blood

Steve Barlow – Steve Skidmore